Sam

Unit 8 Reader

Skills Strand

KINDERGARTEN

Amplify learning.

Table of Contents

Sam

Unit 8 Reader

Sam and the Fish

This is Sam.

Sam and his dad fish in a pond.

Sam's dad brings a rod.

Sam brings a net.

pond

Sam and his dad sit and sit.

Then, zap!

Sam's dad gets a fish.

The fish jumps.

The fish twists and swims.

Sam's dad tugs on the rod.

The fish swims past Sam.

Sam swings his net.

Sam lifts up the net.

The fish is in the net!

Sam and his dad grin.

Fun at the Pond

Sam is at the pond with his pals.

Six frogs rest in the wet mud.

Sam runs at the frogs.

The frogs all hop in the pond.

Sam's pal, Chad, digs up a crab.

The crab gets mad at Chad.

The crab snips at Chad's hands.

Chad drops the crab.

Jen lifts up a log and spots a bug.

The bug is long with lots of legs.

The bug runs and digs in the sand.

The pond is lots of fun.

Sam's Pets

Sam has pets.

One of his pets is a dog.

One of his pets is a cat.

One of his pets is a bug.

This is Sam's dog, Max.

Max runs and jumps.

Max digs in the mud.

Max rubs mud on Sam.

Max yelps at the cat.

This is Sam’s cat, Tim.

Tim sips milk from a dish.

Tim naps on Sam’s bed.

Tim runs from Max.

This is Sam's bug, King Tut.

King Tut hops from plant to plant.

King Tut chomps on plants.

King Tut runs from Tim.

Tasks

Sam has a long list of tasks.

Sam must scrub a bunch of cups.

Sam must help his dad trim shrubs.

Sam must mop the steps.

sam's tasks
scrub cups
mop

Sam scrubs <u>all</u> <u>of</u> the cups.

Scrub, scrub, scrub.

Sam helps his dad trim shrubs.

Snip, snip, snip.

The sun is hot.

Sam gets hot.

Sam spots a fan on the rug.

Sam flops on the rug and naps.

Then his mom spots him.

Sam's mom taps him with the mop.

Sam jumps up. Sam picks up the mop.

The Van

Sam's mom has a van.

Sam is in the van.

Sam and his mom got his pal, Chad.

Then the van hit a big bump.

The van will jump up, up, up.

Then, slam!

The van hit the land.

Crash!

Smash!

Crunch!

Snap!

Pop!

The van w<u>as</u> bent.

The van had lots <u>of</u> dents.

The van did not run.

Sam's mom got a fix-it man.

The fix-it man had a big fix-it kit.

The fix-it kit did not help much.

The fix-it man did not fix the van.

Sam's mom got a cab.

The kids got in the cab.

Sam's mom was sad.

Sam held his mom's hand.

Then Sam sang his mom a song.

"Mom," Sam sang,

"a van is just a van!"

On the Bus

The van is in the fix-it shop.

Sam's mom must get on the bus.

The bus pulls in at the bus stop.

Sam's mom gets on and sits in ba**ck**.

The bus bumps up the hi**ll**.

Sam's mom hangs on with one hand.

Sam's mom rings the be**ll**.

The bus stops at the next stop.

Sam's mom gets o**ff**.

ELM

Sam in Class

Sam sits in Mi**ss** Ma**ck**'s cla**ss**.

The kids will print ti**ll** cla**ss** ends.

Then the be**ll** wi**ll** ring.

Sam wi**ll** run and jump in the pond.

Mi**ss** Ma**ck** has the cla**ss** print.

The kids print *bla**ck** cat.*

Mi**ss** Ma**ck** che**ck**s Sam's print.

"That's a me**ss**!" quips Mi**ss** Ma**ck**.

"Fix it!"

mom
dad
black

The be**ll** rings.

Sam jumps up and grabs his bag.

Mi**ss** Ma**ck** te**ll**s Sam,

"Sit and print!"

0 1 2 3 4
Ee
Ll
Ss
Xx
!
$

Sam sits and prints.

Wi**ll** Mi**ss** Ma**ck** let him swim?

Sam can't te**ll**.

Aa Bb Cc Dd
Ee Ff Gg Hh
Jj Kk Ll
Oo Pp
Rr Ss Tt
Vv Ww Xx
Yy Zz & !
% @ $

Mi**ss** Ma**ck** te**ll**s Sam,

“Print one last thing.

Print *splash in the pond.*”

Sam grins at Mi**ss** Ma**ck**.

Mi**ss** Ma**ck** grins ba**ck** at him.

Sam prints *splash in the pond.*

Then Mi**ss** Ma**ck** sends him o**ff**.

Sam ye**ll**s, “Mi**ss** Ma**ck** is the best!”

hijklmnopqrstuvwxyz
1 2
6 7 8 9
13 14 15 16
20 21 22 23
27 28 29 30

The Chills

Sam met Chad at the pond.

Chad left his pants on the sand.

Sam left his pants on a big ro**ck**.

Chad got in.

Splash!

Then Sam got in.

Splish!

Sam and Chad go

swi**mm**ing in the pond.

The sun was hot,

but the pond was not.

Chad and Sam got the

chi**ll**s.

Sam ran up on the ro**ck**

and got his pants.

Chad ran up on the sand,

but Max, the dog, had his pants.

Chad ran and got his pants

ba**ck** from Max.

Stop That Bus!

Sam's mom runs in and yel**ll**s,

"Sam, get up!"

Sam jumps up.

Sam's mom hands him his pants.

Sam jumps in his pants.

Sam's mom hands him his pa**ck**.

Sam slips the pa**ck** on his ba**ck**.

Sam's mom hands him his lunch.

Sam grabs it.

Sam and his mom run fast.

"That's the bus!" Sam ye**ll**s.

Sam's mom hu**ff**s and pu**ff**s.

"Stop the bus!" Sam ye**ll**s.

BUS
F-19

The kids on the bus spot Sam.

One of them yells, “That’s Sam.

Stop the bus!”

The bus stops.

Sam is in luck.

Sam gets on the bus.

ELM ST
SPRING ST

Sam and the Duck

Sam's cla**ss** is on a trip.

The cla**ss** is at the do**ck**.

Mi**ss** Ma**ck** spots Ken, the fish man.

"Ken," Mi**ss** Ma**ck** asks,

"Can the kids dig in the sand?"

Ken nods.

"Yes, the kids can dig in the sand,

but the kids must not pet the du**ck**.

That du**ck** is a bad du**ck**.

That du**ck** pe**ck**s at kids."

Mi**ss** Ma**ck** te**ll**s the kids,

"Cla**ss**, let's not pet the du**ck**."

Sam and Chad dig in the sand.

Chad digs up a ring.

Sam lifts the ring up.

The ring glints in the sun.

The du**ck** spots the ring.

The du**ck** quacks and runs at Sam.

"Sam!" Mi**ss** Ma**ck** ye**ll**s,

"It's that bad du**ck**,

the one that pe**ck**s!"

The du**ck** runs up and pe**ck**s at Sam's hand.

Then it runs o**ff** with the ring.

"Man!" ye**ll**s Chad.

"That is one bad du**ck**!"

fish

Max in the Mud

Max tra**ck**s mud on the de**ck**.

Sam's mom ye**ll**s, "Bad dog!"

Sam's mom has Sam get a mop.

Sam gets a mop

and mops up the mud.

Sam's mom sni**ff**s Max.

Ug!

The dog sme**ll**s bad!

Sam gets Max in the bath tub.

Sam's mom scrubs him.

Then, at last, Max sme**ll**s fresh!

The Band

Sam's dad is in a ja**zz** band.

That's him in the ba**ck**.

Chad's dad is in the band with him.

That's him on the drums.

Chad's bo**ss** is in the band, as we**ll**.

That's him on the left, in the hat.

jazz
cats

Sam's dad plu**ck**s at his strings.

Chad's dad bangs on his drums.

The kids clap and ye**ll**.

The band is a big hit!

The Chick

Sam and Chad got up on a ro**ck**.

On top of the ro**ck** was a gu**ll**'s nest.

The gu**ll** had a chi**ck**.

The gu**ll** fed the chi**ck** a bit of fish.

Then the gu**ll** left.

The chi**ck** fe**ll** from its nest.

Plop!

The chi**ck** got stu**ck** in a cra**ck**.

Sam and Chad got the chi**ck**.

Then Chad set it ba**ck** in its nest.

About this Book

This book has been created for use by students learning to read with the Core Knowledge Reading Program. Readability levels are suitable for early readers. The book has also been carefully leveled in terms of its "code load," or the number of spellings used in the stories.

The English writing system is complex. It uses more than 200 spellings to stand for 40-odd sounds. Many sounds can be spelled several different ways, and many spellings can be pronounced several different ways. This book has been designed to make early reading experiences simpler and more productive by using a subset of the available spellings. It uses *only* spellings students have been taught to sound out as part of their phonics lessons, plus a handful of tricky words, which have also been deliberately introduced in the lessons. This means the stories will be 100% decodable if they are assigned at the proper time.

As the students move through the program, they learn new spellings and the "code load" in the decodable readers increases gradually. The code load graphic on this page indicates the number of spellings students are expected to know in order to read the first story of the book and the number of spellings students are expected to know in order to read the final stories in the book. The columns on the inside back cover list the specific spellings and Tricky Words students are expected to recognize at the beginning of this reader. The bullets at the bottom of the inside back cover identify spellings, tricky words, and other topics that are introduced gradually in the unit this reader accompanies.

Visit us on the web at www.coreknowledge.org

Core Knowledge Language Arts

Acknowledgments

These materials are the result of the work, advice, and encouragement of numerous individuals over many years. Some of those singled out here already know the depth of our gratitude; others may be surprised to find themselves thanked publicly for help they gave quietly and generously for the sake of the enterprise alone. To helpers named and unnamed we are deeply grateful.

Contributors to Earlier Versions of these Materials
Susan B. Albaugh, Kazuko Ashizawa, Nancy Braier, Kathryn M. Cummings, Michelle De Groot, Diana Espinal, Mary E. Forbes, Michael L. Ford, Ted Hirsch, Danielle Knecht, James K. Lee, Diane Henry Leipzig, Martha G. Mack, Liana Mahoney, Isabel McLean, Steve Morrison, Juliane K. Munson, Elizabeth B. Rasmussen, Laura Tortorelli, Rachael L. Shaw, Sivan B. Sherman, Miriam E. Vidaver, Catherine S. Whittington, Jeannette A. Williams

We would like to extend special recognition to Program Directors Matthew Davis and Souzanne Wright who were instrumental to the early development of this program.

Schools
We are truly grateful to the teachers, students, and administrators of the following schools for their willingness to field test these materials and for their invaluable advice: Capitol View Elementary, Challenge Foundation Academy (IN), Community Academy Public Charter School, Lake Lure Classical Academy, Lepanto Elementary School, New Holland Core Knowledge Academy, Paramount School of Excellence, Pioneer Challenge Foundation Academy, New York City PS 26R (The Carteret School), PS 30X (Wilton School), PS 50X (Clara Barton School), PS 96Q, PS 102X (Joseph O. Loretan), PS 104Q (The Bays Water), PS 214K (Michael Friedsam), PS 223Q (Lyndon B. Johnson School), PS 308K (Clara Cardwell), PS 333Q (Goldie Maple Academy), Sequoyah Elementary School, South Shore Charter Public School, Spartanburg Charter School, Steed Elementary School, Thomas Jefferson Classical Academy, Three Oaks Elementary, West Manor Elementary.

And a special thanks to the CKLA Pilot Coordinators Anita Henderson, Yasmin Lugo-Hernandez, and Susan Smith, whose suggestions and day-to-day support to teachers using these materials in their classrooms was critical.

Credits

Illustrations

All illustrations by Dustin Mackay